The Wonky Donkey

For my mum,
and all the people who have helped me
over the years: family, friends and mentors.
Thank you.
– Craig Smith

To my precious Mum, Dad and aunt Wren ...
your love, support and inspiration fuels my creative journey
and makes all of me smile and sing. With big-fat gratitude
for keeping me tuned to the magic and humour of life.
– Katz Cowley

First published in 2009 by Scholastic New Zealand Limited
This reformatted edition published in 2010 by Scholastic New Zealand Limited,
Private Bag 94407, Greenmount, Auckland 2141, New Zealand

Scholastic Australia Pty Limited
PO Box 579, Gosford, NSW 2250, Australia

Text © Craig Smith, 2007
Illustrations © Katz Cowley, 2009

ISBN 978-1-86943-985-9

National Library of New Zealand Cataloguing-in-Publication Data

Smith, Craig, 1972–
Wonky Donkey / by Craig Smith ; illustrated by Katz Cowley.
ISBN 978-1-86943-985-9
Previous ed.: 2009.
1. Children's songs—Texts. [1. Donkeys—Songs and music.
2. Songs.] I. Cowley, Katz. II. Title.
782.42083—dc 22

12 11 10 9 8 7 6 5 4 3   0 1 2 3 4 5 6 7 8 9 / 1

Illustrations created in watercolours.

Publishing team: Diana Murray, Penny Scown and Annette Bisman
Design by Book Design Ltd, Christchurch, www.bookdesign.co.nz

The Wonky Donkey

Words and music by **Craig Smith**

Illustrations by **Katz Cowley**

SCHOLASTIC

AUCKLAND SYDNEY NEW YORK LONDON TORONTO
MEXICO CITY NEW DELHI HONG KONG

I was walking down the road
and I saw ...

a donkey,

Hee Haw!

And he only had three legs!

He was a
wonky donkey.

I was walking down the road
and I saw a donkey,

He only had three legs ...

and one eye!

He was a winky wonky donkey.

I was walking down the road
and I saw a donkey,

Hee Haw!

He only had three legs,
one eye ...

and he liked to listen to country music.

Yee Haa!

He was a honky-tonky
winky wonky donkey.

I was walking down the road
and I saw a donkey,

Hee Haw!

He only had three legs,
one eye,
he liked to listen to country music ...

and he was quite tall and slim.

He was
a lanky
honky-
tonky
winky
wonky
donkey.

I was walking down the road
and I saw a donkey,

Hee Haw!

He only had three legs,
one eye,
he liked to listen to country music,
he was quite tall and slim ...

and he smelt really, really bad.

He was a stinky-dinky
lanky honky-tonky
winky wonky donkey.

I was walking down the road
and I saw a donkey,

Hee Haw!

He only had three legs,
one eye,
he liked to listen to country music,
he was quite tall and slim,
he smelt really, really bad ...

and that morning he'd got up early
and hadn't had any coffee.

He was a cranky
stinky-dinky lanky
honky-tonky
winky wonky donkey.

I was walking down the road
and I saw a donkey,

Hee How!

He only had three legs,
one eye,
he liked to listen to country music,
he was quite tall and slim,
he smelt really, really bad,
that morning he'd got up early
and hadn't had any coffee ...

and he was always getting up to mischief.

He was a hanky-panky cranky stinky-dinky lanky honky-tonky winky wonky donkey.

I was walking down the road
and I saw a donkey,

Hee Haw!

He only had three legs,

one eye,

he liked to listen to country music,

he was quite tall and slim,

he smelt really, really bad,

that morning he'd got up early

and hadn't had any coffee,

he was always getting up to mischief ...

but he was quite good looking!

He was a spunky hanky-panky cranky
stinky-dinky lanky honky-tonky winky wonky donkey!

I was walking down the road

and I saw a donkey ...

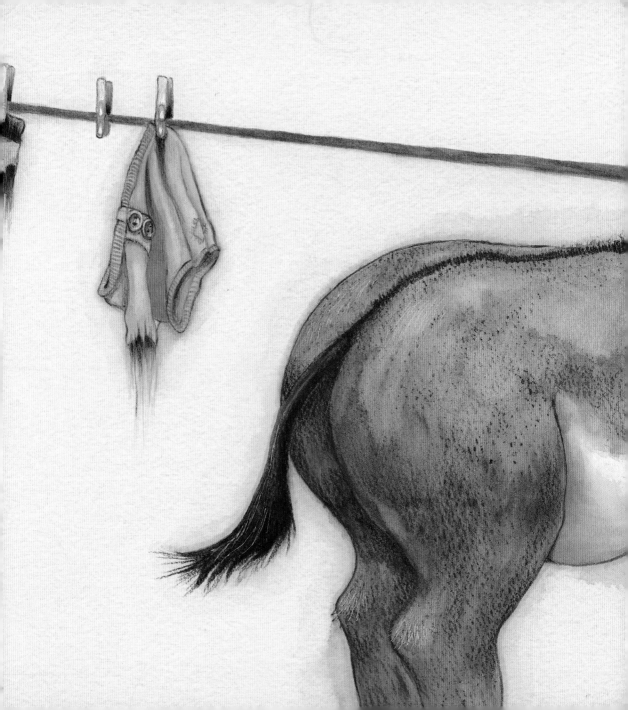